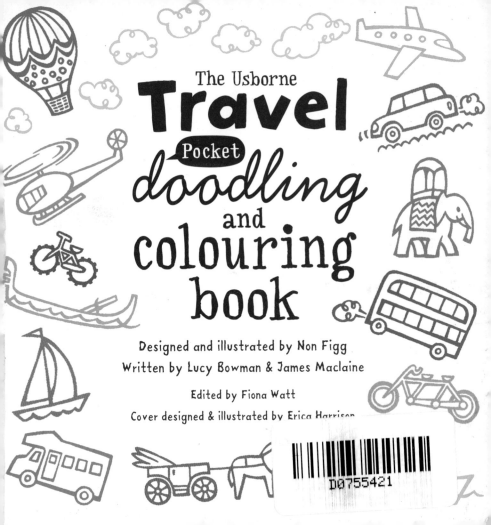

The Usborne
Travel
Pocket
doodling
and
colouring
book

Designed and illustrated by Non Figg

Written by Lucy Bowman & James Maclaine

Edited by Fiona Watt

Cover designed & illustrated by Erica Harrison

Fill in the fish.

2

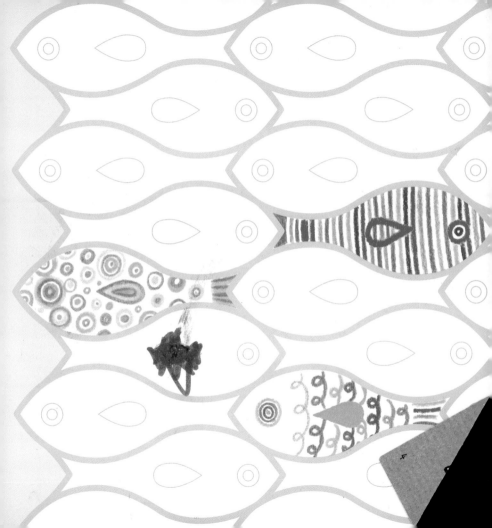

Colour in the postcards.

Doodle buses, cars, boats, planes...

6

...bikes, helicopters and hot-air balloons, too.

Using the triangles as a guide, fill the pages with mountains and trees.

Fill the shapes with patterns.

12

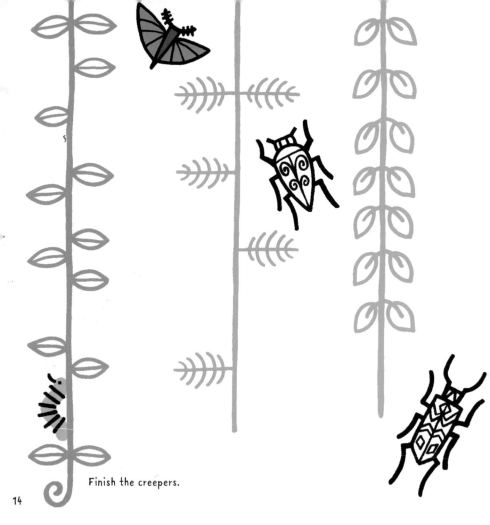

Finish the creepers.

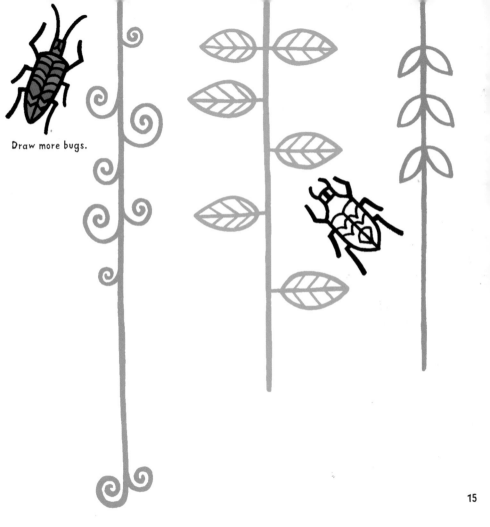

Draw more bugs.

Add cars, trucks and vans to the town.

16

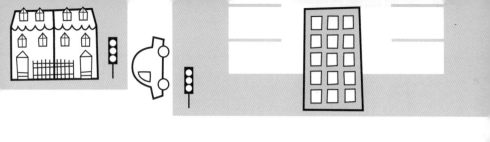

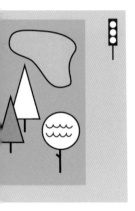

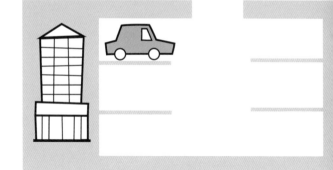

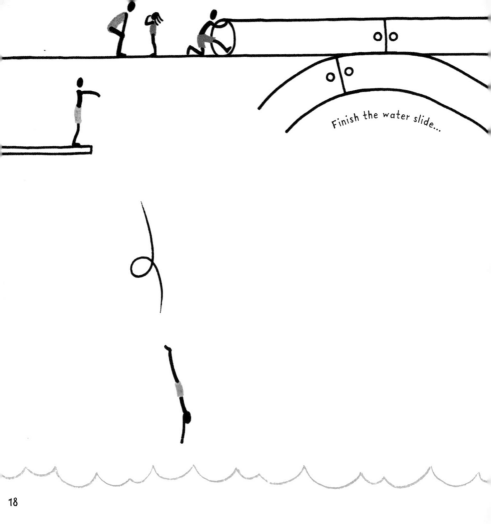

Finish the water slide...

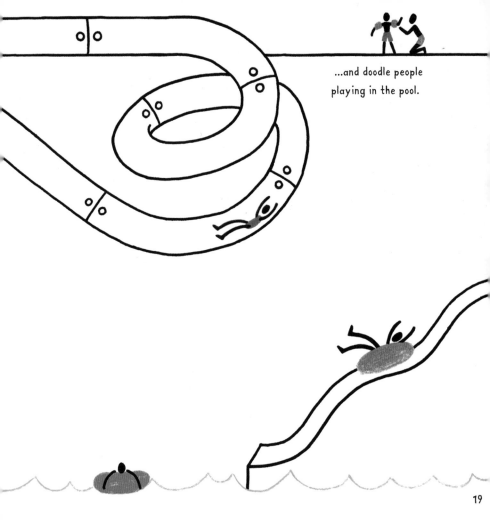

...and doodle people
playing in the pool.

Turn these shapes into seaside buildings.

Finish each line without taking your pen off the paper.

23

Colour...colour...

24

Decorate the camper vans.

Draw people in kayaks.

28

Add passengers, portholes and lifeboats.

Then, finish the railings.

Doodle faces, then add some colour.

32

33

Doodle flowers...

...patterns...

...and leaves.

35

Turn the shapes into planes.

Draw birds on the wires.

Doodle penguins...

...and seals.

Finish drawing this city scene...

42

...and colour it in.

43

Doodle more waves, boats and storm clouds.

45

Colour in the train...

46

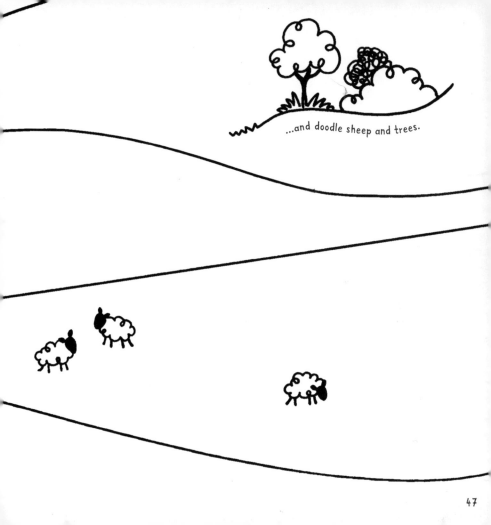

...and doodle sheep and trees.

49

Draw roads winding in and out of each other.

Then, scribble in the gaps with a green pen.

1.30

1.50

20

60

78

Colour in the stamps
and design your own.

53

Use coloured pencils to add more buildings.

54

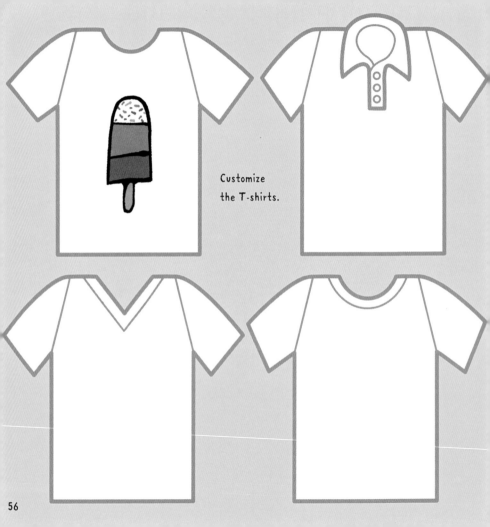

Customize
the T-shirts.

Give these penguins
skis and poles.

58

Some might like hats and scarves.

Draw barnacles on the anchors.

60

Finish the ropes, too.

Turn these
shapes into
exotic birds.

62

Doodle on the clouds...

...and draw a face on the Sun.

Draw on the shapes to turn them into shells.

Colour...colour...

69

Add patterns to these
starfish and sea anemones.

70

Decorate the hot-air balloons.

Add disguises to the people in the passport photos.

74

Fill the pages with suitcases and bags.

Decorate the
Egyptians...

Doodle more pyramids.

...and draw
what the slaves
are carrying.

79

Turn the circles into wheels for different vehicles.

Doodle different faces.

82

83

Doodle lots of waves across the pages.

Turn these shapes into cars and buses.

Colour in the patterns on the camels' blankets...

...and design your own.

Draw people on the slopes...

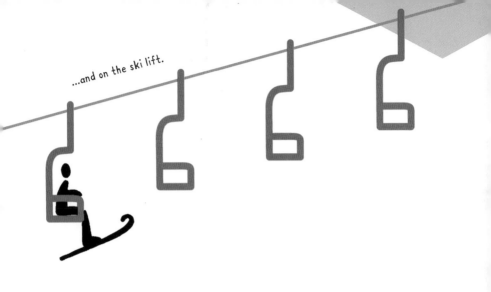

...and on the ski lift.

Colour in the tents...

...and add some patterns.

92

Keep doodling holiday villas across the pages.

Add passengers in the windows and luggage on the roof.

Finish this paw print pattern.

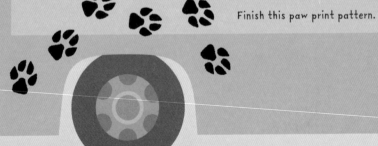

Add birds in the sky and sailing boats on the sea.

Doodle more palm trees and waves without taking your pen off the paper.

Colour in the luggage labels.

102

Doodle planes, clouds, trees and hills.

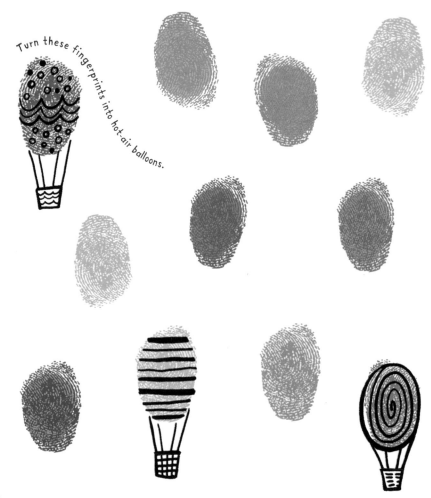

Turn these fingerprints into hot-air balloons.

Colour in the jellyfish.

Draw different vehicles on the grid.

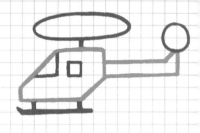

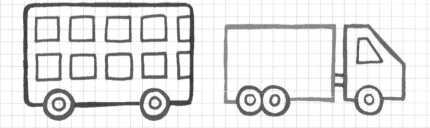

112

Decorate the ice creams with toppings.

114

Draw stripes on the zebras.

Doodle patterns, too.

Carry on drawing this tropical surfing scene.

Add tiles, railings, balconies...

...and people, too.

121

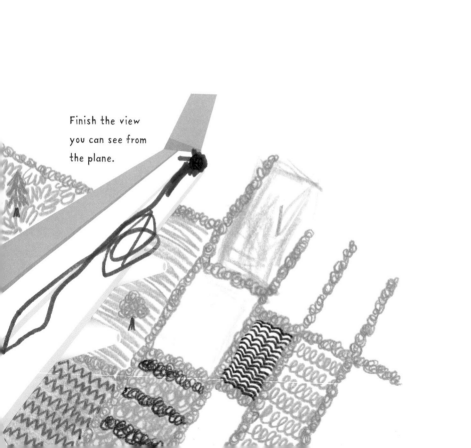

Finish the view
you can see from
the plane.

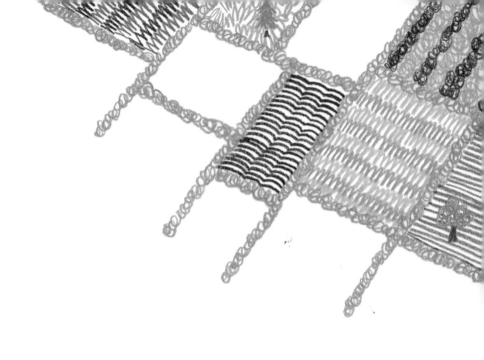

Decorate the drying
towels and add plants
in the pots.

Turn the shapes into submarines.

Doodle fish in the sea, too.